## CONTENTS

© 2008 by Faber Music Ltd
First published in 1987 by International Music Publications Ltd
International Music Publications Ltd is a Faber Music company
3 Queen Square, London WC1N 3AU
Edited by Peter Foss
Printed in England by Caligraving Ltd
All rights reserved

ISBN10: 0-571-53272-1
EAN13: 978-0-571-53272-8

# All I Want For Christmas Is My Two Front Teeth

Words and Music
by DON GARDNER

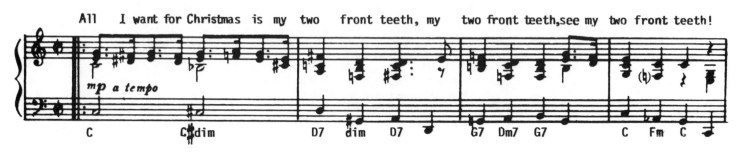

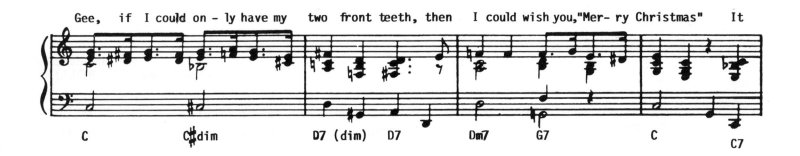

Gee, if I could on-ly have my two front teeth, then I could wish you, "Mer-ry Christmas" It

C    C#dim    D7 (dim) D7    Dm7    G7    C    C7

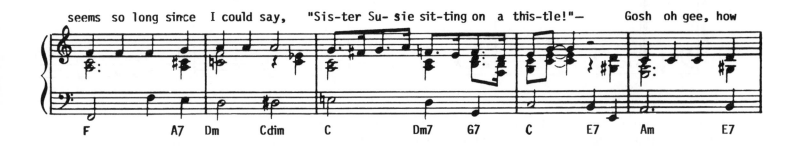

seems so long since I could say, "Sis-ter Su-sie sit-ting on a this-tle!"— Gosh oh gee, how

F    A7 Dm    Cdim    C    Dm7 G7    C    E7    Am    E7

hap-py I'd be, if I could on-ly whis-tle— (thhh.) All I want for Christmas is my

Am    E7    Am Am7    D7 D7-9 Am7 D7    Cdim G7    C    C#dim

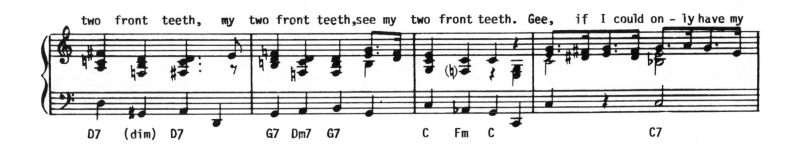

two front teeth, my two front teeth, see my two front teeth. Gee, if I could on-ly have my

D7    (dim) D7    G7 Dm7 G7    C Fm C    C7

two front teeth, then I could wish you "Merry Christmas!"    Christmas!"

F A7 Dm7 Cdim    C Gdim G7    Cmaj7 C Cdim G7    Cmaj7 C    Gdim Dm7    Fdim C

# Frosty The Snowman

Words and Music by
STEVE NELSON and JACK ROLLINS

# The First Nowell

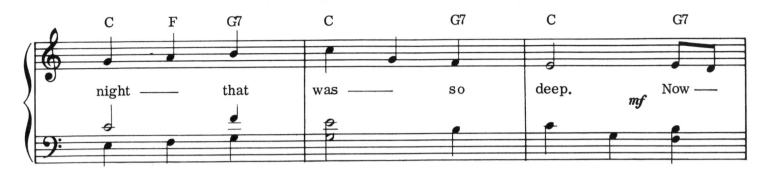

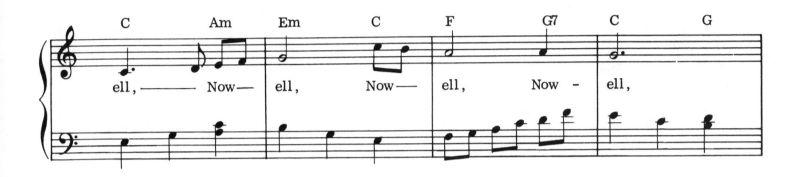

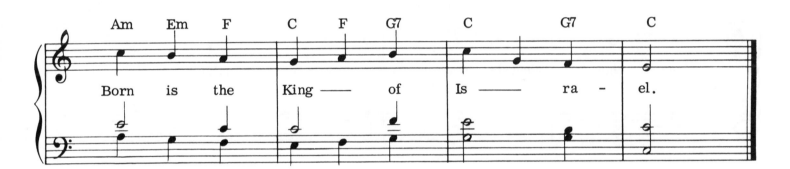

2. They look-ed up and saw a star
   Shining in the east beyond them far
   And to the earth it gave great light
   And so it continued both day and night
   Nowell, etc.

3. And by the light of that same star
   Three wise men came from country far;
   To seek for a king was their intent
   And to follow the star wherever it went.
   Nowell, etc.

4. This star drew nigh to the north-west,
   O'er Bethlehem it took its rest
   And there it did both stop and stay
   Right over the place where Jesus lay.
   Nowell, etc.

5. Then let us all with one accord
   Sing praises to our heavenly Lord
   That hath made heaven and earth of nought
   And with His blood mankind hath bought.
   Nowell, etc.

# Good King Wenceslas

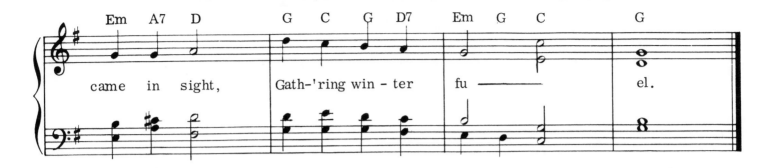

2. "Hither, page, and stand by me,
   If thou know'st it, telling
   Yonder peasant, who is he?
   Where, and what his dwelling?"
   "Sire, he lives a good league hence,
   Underneath the mountain;
   Right against the forest fence,
   By St. Agnes fountain."

3. "Bring me flesh and bring me wine,
   Bring me pine logs hither;
   Thou and I will see him dine,
   When we bear them thither."
   Page and monarch forth they went,
   Onward both together,
   Through the rude winds wild lament,
   And the bitter weather.

4. "Sire, the night is darker now
   And the wind blows stronger;
   Fails my heart, I know not how,
   I can go no longer."
   "Mark my footsteps, good my page!
   Tread thou in them boldly;
   Thou shall find the winter's rage
   Freeze thy blood less coldly."

5. In his master's steps he trod,
   Where the snow lay dinted;
   Heat was in the very sod
   Which the saint had printed.
   Therefore, Christian men, be sure -
   Wealth or rank possessing -
   Ye, who now will bless the poor,
   Shall yourselves find blessing.

# Hark The Herald Angels Sing

2. Christ by highest heav'n adored,
   Christ, the everlasting Lord;
   Late in time behold Him come,
   Offspring of a Virgin's womb.
   Veiled in flesh the God-head see!
   Hail th'incarnate Deity!
   Pleased as man with man to dwell,
   Jesus, our Immanuel.
   Hark! The herald angels sing,
   Glory to the new-born King.

3. Hail, the heaven born Prince of peace!
   Hail, the Son of righteousness!
   Light and life to all He brings,
   Risen with healing in His wings,
   Mild He lays His glory by;
   Born that man no more may die;
   Born to raise the sons of earth;
   Born, to give them second birth.
   Hark! the herald angels sing,
   Glory to the new-born King!

# Have Yourself A Merry Little Christmas

Words and Music by
HUGH MARTIN and RALPH BLANE

# The Holly And The Ivy

# The Christmas Song
# (Chestnuts Roasting On An Open Fire)

Words and Music by
MEL TORME and ROBERT WELLS

# I Saw Mommy Kissing Santa Claus

Words and Music
by TOMMIE CONNOR

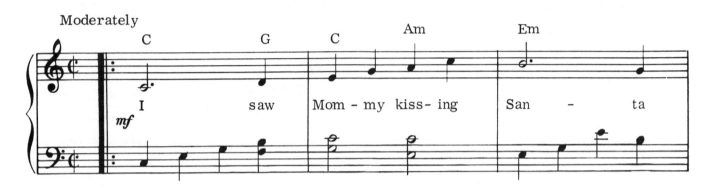

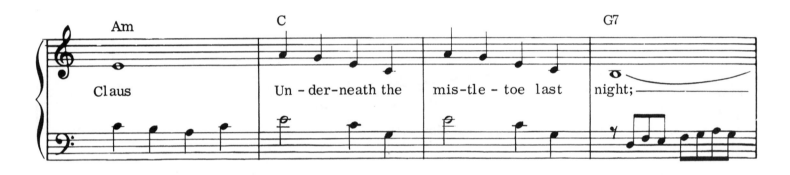

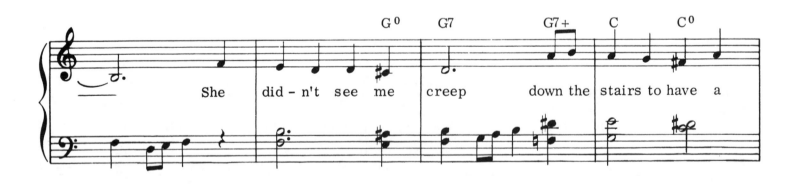

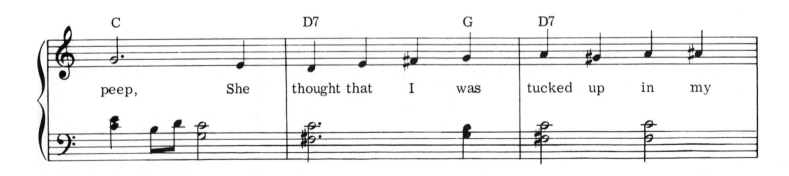

# Jingle Bells

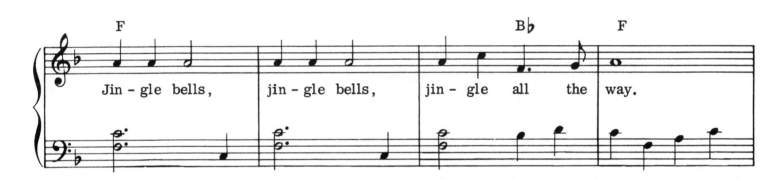

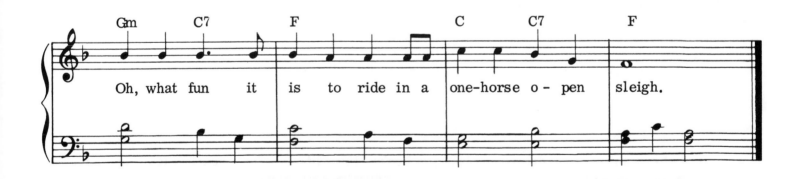

2. Now the ground is white
   Go it while you're young.
   Take the girls tonight,
   Sing this sleighing song.
   Get a bob-tailed bay,
   Two-forty for his speed.
   Then hitch him to an open sleigh
   And you will take the lead.
   Jingle bells, etc.

# The Little Boy That Santa Claus Forgot

Words and Music by MICHAEL CARR,
TOMMIE CONNOR and JIMMY LEACH

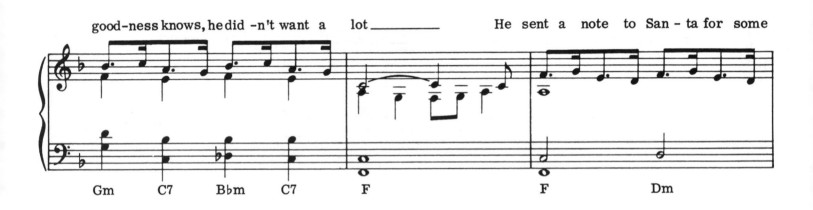

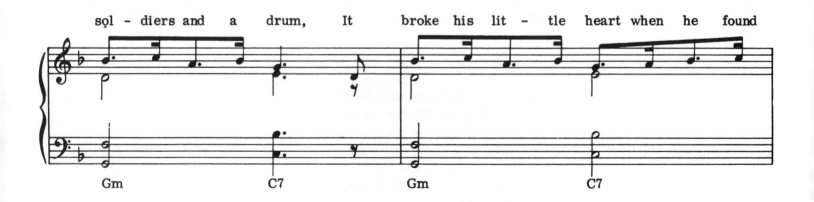

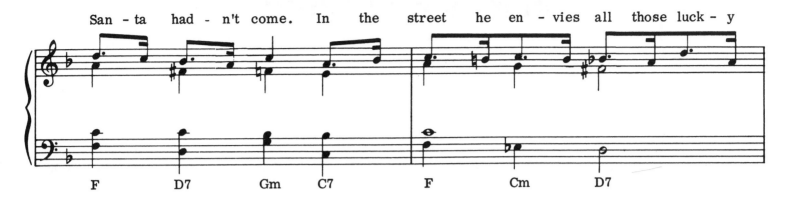

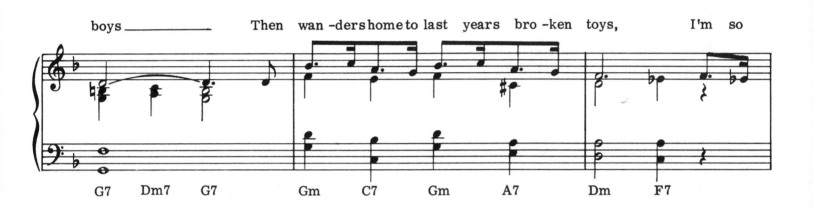

# Mary's Boy Child

Words and Music
by JESTER HAIRSTON

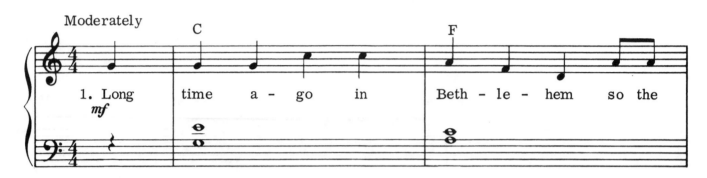

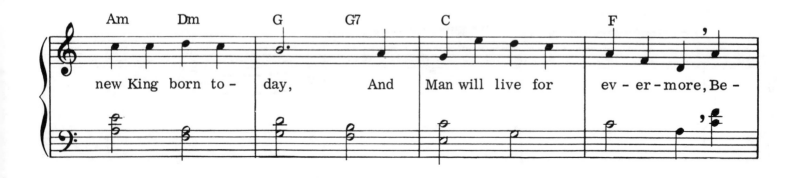

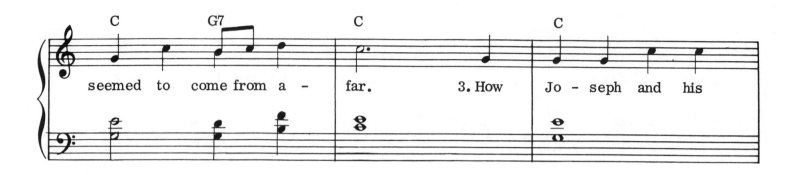

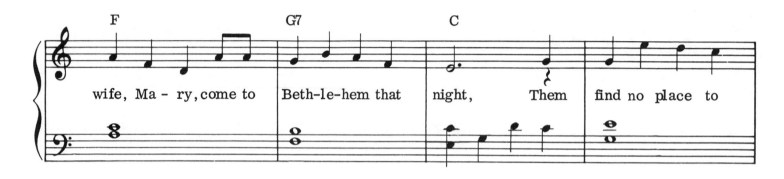

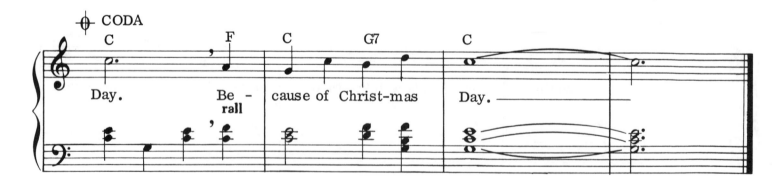

4. By and by they find a little nook
   In a stable all forlorn,
   And in a manger cold and dark,
   Mary's little boy was born.

5. Long time ago in Bethlehem,
   So the Holy Bible say,
   Mary's Boy Child, Jesus Christ,
   Was born on Christmas Day.

# Little Donkey

Words and Music
by ERIC BOSWELL

Moderately

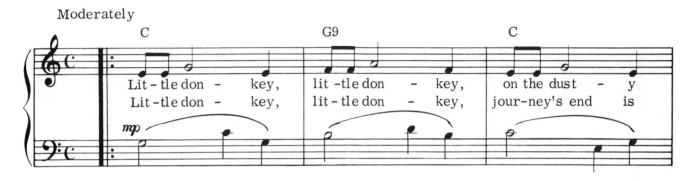

Lit - tle don - key, lit - tle don - key, on the dust - y
Lit - tle don - key, lit - tle don - key, jour - ney's end is

road. Got to keep on plod-ding on - wards
near. There are wise men wait-ing for a

with your pre - cious load. Been a long time,
sign to bring them here. Do not fal - ter,

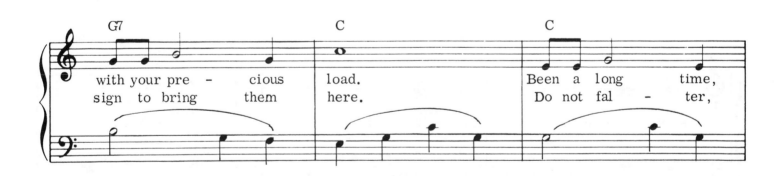

lit - tle don - key, thro' the win - ter's night.
lit - tle don - key, there's a star a - head.

# The Little Drummer Boy

Words and Music by HARRY SIMEONE,
HENRY ONORATI and KATHERINE K DAVIS

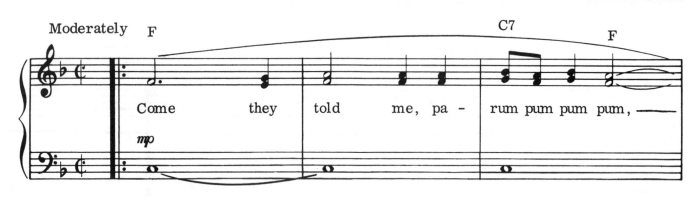

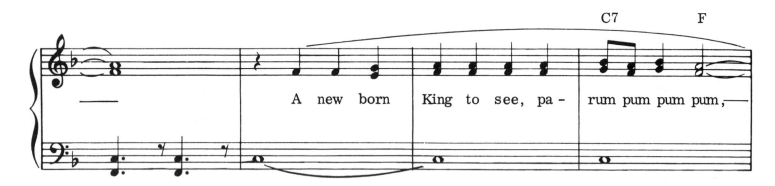

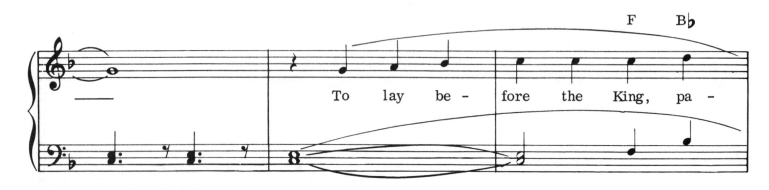

rum pum pum pum,    rum pum pum pum,    rum pum pum pum,———

So    to    hon - our Him,  pa - rum pum pum  pum,———

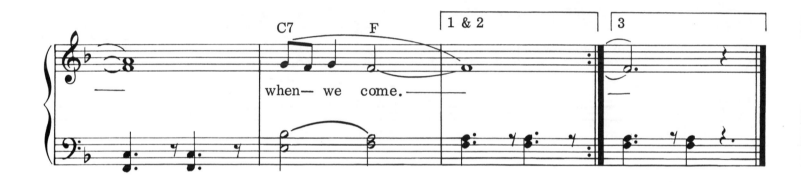

when— we   come.———

2. Little Baby, pa-rum pum pum pum,
   I am a poor boy too, pa-rum pum pum pum,
   I have no gift to bring, pa-rum pum pum pum,
   That's fit to give our King, pa-rum pum pum pum,
   Rum pum pum pum, rum pum pum pum,
   Shall I play for you, pa-rum pum pum pum,
   On my drum?

3. Mary nodded, pa-rum pum pum pum,
   The Ox and Lamb kept time, pa-rum pum pum pum,
   I played my drum for Him, pa-rum pum pum pum,
   I played my best for Him, pa-rum pum pum pum,
   Rum pum pum pum, rum pum pum pum,
   Then He smiled at me, pa-rum pum pum pum,
   Me and my drum.

# Mister Santa
# (Mister Sandman)

Words and Music
by PAT BALLARD

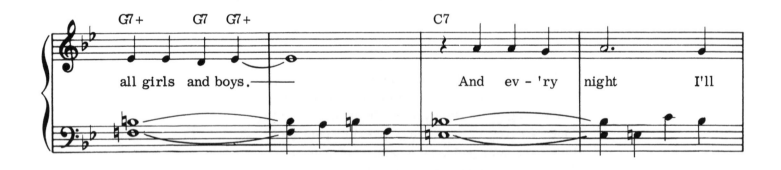

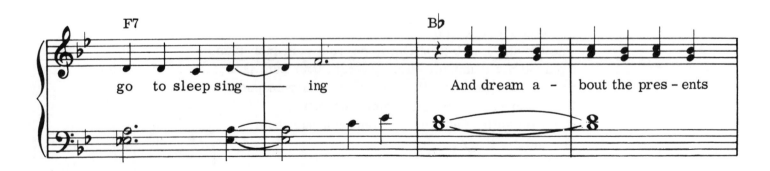

# O Come All Ye Faithful

2. God of God,
   Light of light,
   Lo! He abhors not the virgin's womb;
   Very God, begotten, not created;
   O come, let us etc.

3. Sing, choirs of Angels,
   Sing in exultation,
   Sing, all ye citizens of heav'n above:
   'Glory to God in the highest;'
   O come, let us etc.

4. Yea, Lord, we greet Thee,
   Born this happy morning;
   Jesu, to Thee be glory given;
   Word of the Father, Now in flesh appearing
   O come, let us etc.

# Once In Royal David's City

mild,    Je - sus    Christ    her lit —— tle —— child.

2. He came down to earth from heaven,
   Who is God and Lord of all;
   And His shelter was a stable
   And His cradle was a stall.
   With the poor and mean and lowly
   Lived on earth our Saviour holy.

3. And through all His wondrous childhood
   He would honour and obey,
   Love and watch the lowly Maiden
   In whose gentle arms He lay;
   Christian children all must be
   Mild, obedient, good as He.

4. For He is our childhood's pattern,
   Day by day like us He grew;
   He was little, weak and helpless,
   Tears and smiles like us He knew;
   And He feeleth for our sadness,
   And He shareth in our gladness.

5. And our eyes at last shall see Him
   Through His own redeeming love,
   For that Child so dear and gentle
   Is our Lord in heaven above;
   And He leads His children on
   To the place where He is gone.

6. Not in that poor lowly stable,
   With the oxen standing by,
   We shall see Him; but in heaven,
   Set at God's right hand on high;
   When like stars His children crown'd
   All in white shall wait around.

# Rudolph The Red-Nosed Reindeer

Words and Music
by JOHNNY MARKS

# Santa Claus Is Comin' To Town

Words by HAVEN GILLESPIE
Music by J FRED COOTS

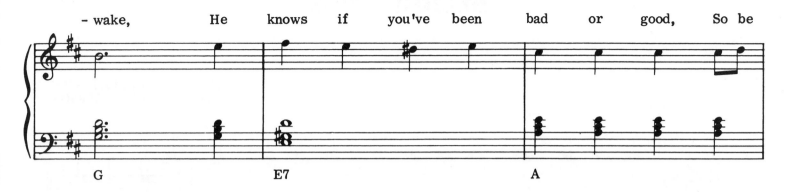

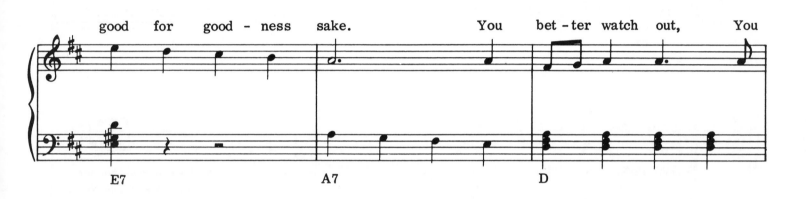

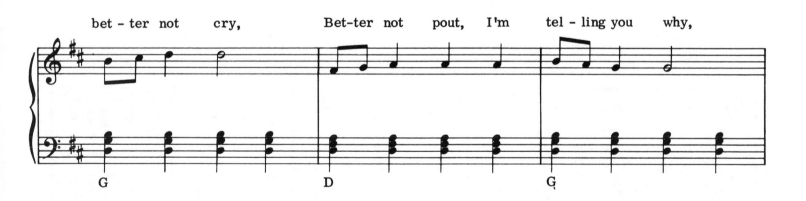

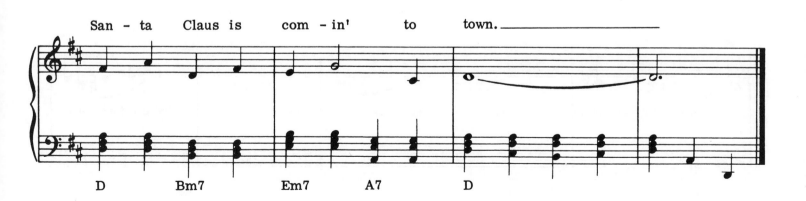

# Sleigh Ride

Words by MITCHELL PARISH
Music by LEROY ANDERSON

**Allegro con ritmo**

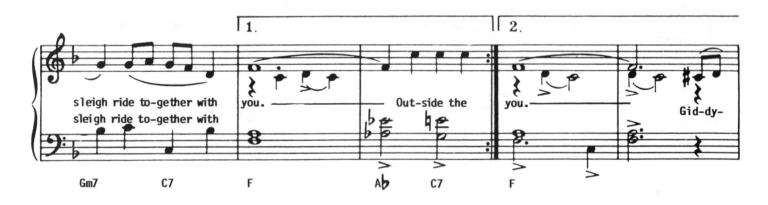

# When A Child Is Born

Words by FRED JAY
Music by ZACAR

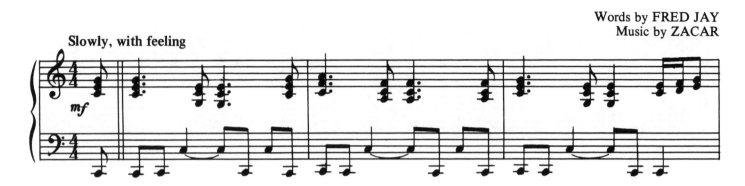

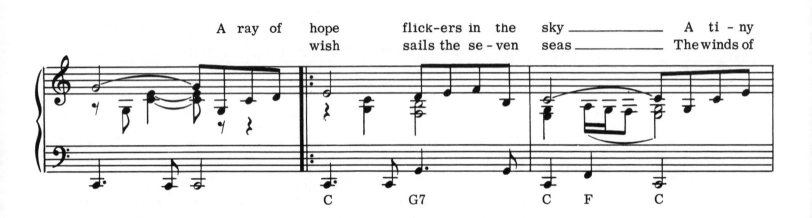

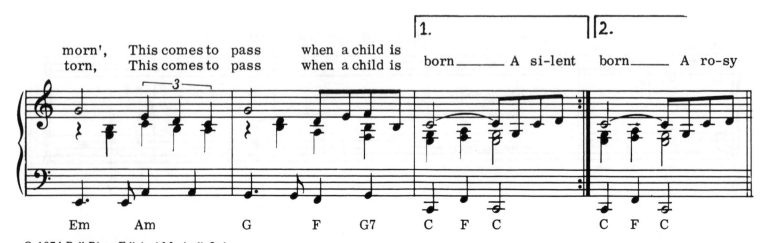

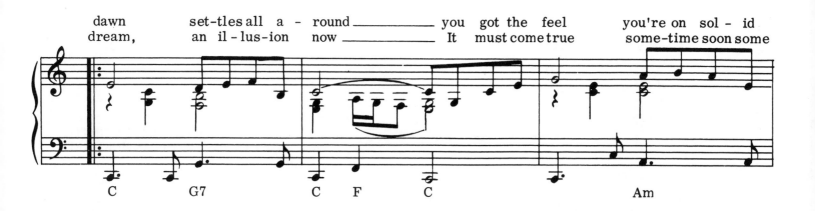

dawn     set-tles all a - round \_\_\_\_\_ you got the feel     you're on sol - id

dream,     an il - lus-ion now \_\_\_\_\_ It must come true     some-time soon some

C     G7     C   F    C        Am

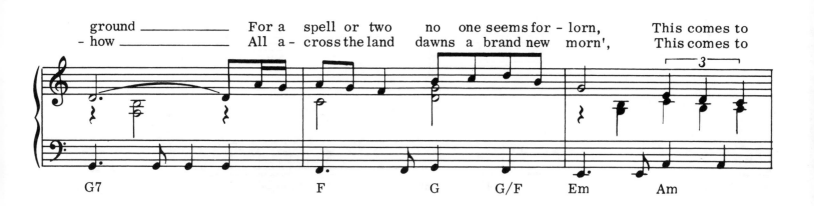

ground \_\_\_\_\_ For a   spell or two    no one seems for - lorn,    This comes to

- how \_\_\_\_\_ All a - cross the land   dawns a brand new morn',    This comes to

G7             F     G    G/F   Em    Am

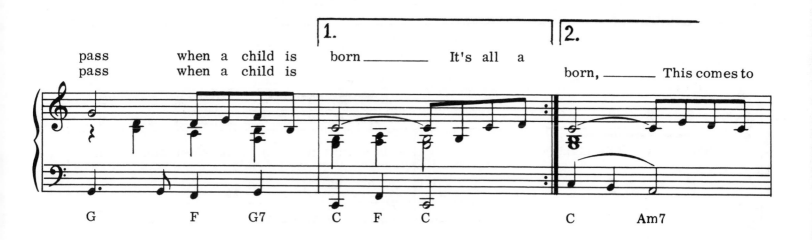

**1.**                  **2.**

pass    when a child is   born \_\_\_\_\_ It's all a

pass    when a child is                born, \_\_\_\_\_ This comes to

G     F    G7    C   F   C        C     Am7

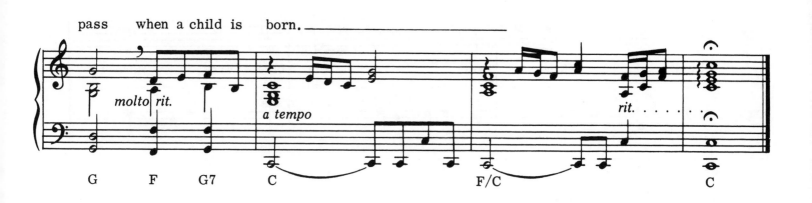

pass    when a child is   born. \_\_\_\_\_

*molto rit.*        *a tempo*                      *rit. . . . . . .*

G    F    G7    C          F/C        C

# Winter Wonderland

Words by DICK SMITH
Music by FELIX BERNARD

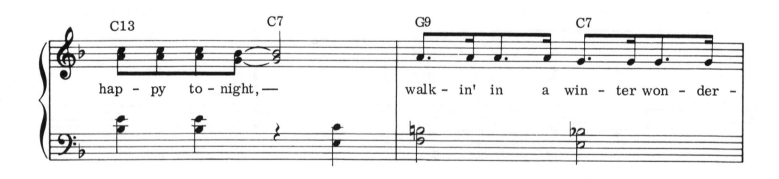

# Silent Night

# THE SONGSCAPE SERIES

## LIN MARSH

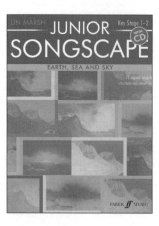
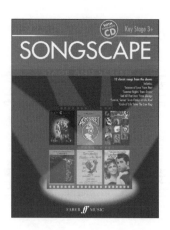
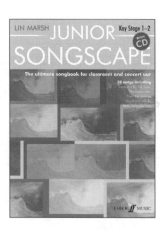

**Key Stage 1–2**

Junior Songscape (Book/CD)
ISBN: 0-571-52077-4

Junior Songscape: Earth, Sea & Sky (Book/CD)
ISBN: 0-571-52206-8

Junior Songscape: Stage & Screen (Book/CD)
ISBN: 0-571-52503-2

Junior Songscape: Children's Favourites (Book/2CDs)
ISBN: 0-571-52644-6

**Key Stage 3**

Songscape (pupil's book)
ISBN: 0-571-51866-4    10-pack: ISBN: 0-571-51944-X

Songscape (teacher's book)
ISBN: 0-571-51867-2

Songscape: Stage & Screen (Book/ECD)
ISBN: 0-571-52609-8

Songscape: Christmas (Book/2CDs)
ISBN: 0-571-52643-8

FABER *ff* MUSIC

To buy Faber Music publications or to find out about the full range of titles available
please contact your local music retailer or Faber Music sales enquiries:

Faber Music Ltd, Burnt Mill, Elizabeth Way, Harlow CM20 2HX
Tel: +44 (0) 1279 82 89 82   Fax: +44 (0) 1279 82 89 83
sales@fabermusic.com   fabermusic.com   expressprintmusic.com

# THE SPOTLIGHT SERIES

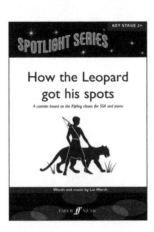

Carnival! *Camille Saint-Saëns & Gwyn Arch*
ISBN: 0-571-51882-6

A Minibeast Christmas (with CD) *Pam Wedgwood & Debbie Needle*
ISBN: 0-571-52194-0

Drum songs *Lin Marsh*
ISBN: 0-571-52218-1

The Christmas Cobweb (with CD) *Pam Wedgwood & Debbie Needle*
ISBN: 0-571-52294-7

Tam Lin (with CD) *Lin Marsh*
ISBN: 0-571-52295-5

How the leopard got his spots *Lin Marsh*
ISBN: 0-571-52298-X

Nativity Nightmares (with CD) *Sheila Wilson*
ISBN: 0-571-52380-3

Prodigal Rock! (with ECD) *Sheila Wilson*
ISBN: 0-571-52650-0

Penny the Raindrop (with CD) *Lin Marsh*
ISBN: 0-571-53251-9

Footprints (with CD) *Lin Marsh*
ISBN: 0-571-53249-7

Toy Box (with CD) *Lin Marsh*
ISBN: 0-571-53250-0

Along came man (with CD) *Lin Marsh*
ISBN: 0-571-53248-9

## Spotlight singles

The Music of Life *Lin Marsh*
ISBN: 0-571-52403-6

Playpiece *Mike Brewer*
ISBN: 0-571-52504-0

To buy Faber Music publications or to find out about the full range of titles available
please contact your local music retailer or Faber Music sales enquiries:

Faber Music Ltd, Burnt Mill, Elizabeth Way, Harlow CM20 2HX
Tel: +44 (0) 1279 82 89 82   Fax: +44 (0) 1279 82 89 83
sales@fabermusic.com   fabermusic.com   expressprintmusic.com